MELANIE C NORTHERN STAR

Wise Publications
London/New York/Sydney/Paris/Copenhagen/Madrid/Tokyo

GO!

Words & Music by Melanie Chisholm & William Orbit.

Verse 2:
I've never been in love before
But this is where it has to end
I just can't love you anymore
Don't even want you as a friend
Can't love you anymore, anymore.

Go. Find what you're looking for *etc.*

NORTHERN STAR

Words & Music by Melanie Chisholm & Rick Nowels.

If all the his-to-ry is_____ true,_____ she's gon-na end up just like
(Verse 2 see block lyric)

you._____ You made it to the oth-er side,

but tell me who will be my_____ guide._____ They build you up so they can

tear you down._____ Trust the o-cean, you'll nev-er drown._____

North - ern star.___ (Ah.___

(Ah.___

(Ah.___

(Ah.___

Verse 2:
Fulfil the longing in your heart
Then we will never be apart
And if they dare to question you
Just tell them that our love is true
They buy your dreams so they can sell your soul
Is it any wonder we've lost control?
Feelings come. Feelings go.

I have learnt my lesson well *etc.*

GOIN' DOWN

Words & Music by Melanie Chisholm, Richard Stannard & Julian Gallagher.

1. How come I did-n't see___ you were mak-ing fun of me?___ How

dare you change the rules,— you made me look a fool.— When are you— gon-na see— the last

laugh's not on me?— What have I— got to do— to get my—

— re - venge on you?— You're go - in' down.—

Go - in' down.— 2. Was it

just a-no-ther line,— or did I mis-read the signs?— What else could I do,— I was so—

(Verse 3 see block lyric)

— in-to you?— With all this bad luck I've had— my

kar-ma must be bad.— You played your lit-tle game,— mmm,—

— what a shame— you're go-in' down.— Go-in' down.

19

Verse 3:
Now I feel no remorse
My life is back on course
From this little hitch
I have become a super-bitch
But don't be afraid
By that confession I made
I am not a whore
I have gone hardcore.

You're goin' down *etc.*

I TURN TO YOU

Words & Music by Melanie Chisholm, Rick Nowels & Billy Steinberg.

1. When the world is dark-er than I can un-der-stand,

(Verse 2 see block lyrics)

Verse 2:
When my insides are wracked with anxiety
You have the touch that will quiet me
You lift my spirit, you melt the ice
When I need inspiration, when I need advice.

I turn to you *etc.*

IF THAT WERE ME

Words & Music by Melanie Chisholm & Rick Nowels.

1. Where do they go_____ and what do they do?_____
(Verses 2 & 3 see block lyrics)

They're walk-ing on by, _____ they're look-ing at you. _____

Some peo-ple stop, _____ some peo-ple stare. _____

But would _____ they help _____ you and do _____ they care? _____

How _____ did _____ you fall? _____ Did you fall _____ at all? _____

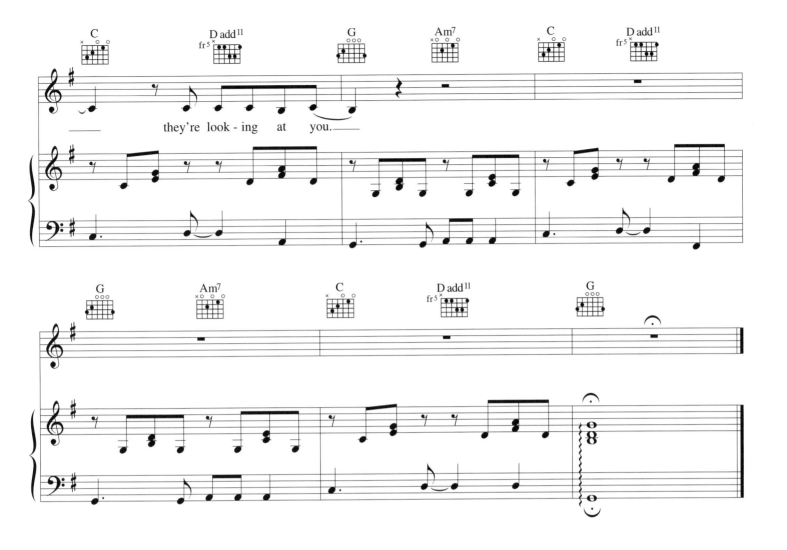

they're look-ing at you.

Verse 2:
A spare bit of change is all that I give
How is that gonna help when you've got nowhere to live?
Some turn away so they don't see
I bet you'd look if that were me.

How did you fall?
Did you fall at all?
Is it lonely where you are, sleeping in between parked cars?
When it thunders where do you hide from the storm?

Verse 3:
Could you ever forgive my self-pity?
When you've got nothing and you're living on the streets of the city
I couldn't live without my phone
But you don't even have a home.

How did we fall?
Can we get up at all?
Are we happy where we are on our lonely little star?
When it's cold is it your hope that keeps you warm?

WHY

Words & Music by Melanie Chisholm, Marius De Vries & Steve Sidelnyk.

that did-n't have—— a chance—— to start.——

A♭   A♭m   E♭

Put out—— the stars,—— rub out—— the sky.—— Look to the fu - ture, wipe—— the tear-

A♭   A♭m

- drop from my eye.—— Shut out—— the sun,—— put out—— the light.——

B♭7(♭9)   G

I want you to tell—— me how—— you're gon - na make—— it right.——

Why_____ am I cry - ing ov - er you?___ Why?_____ Cos there's

no-thing else — that I___ can do.___ Why_____ do I al - ways look___ a fool?_____

Why? I___ I._____

37

Verse 2:
Wish I'd read the signs and left you well alone
God, I wanna call you but I can't pick up the phone
Put out the stars
Rub out the sky
Look to the future
Wipe the teardrop from my eye
Shut out the sun
Bring on the night
Want you to show me how you're gonna make it right

Why am I crying over you? *etc.*

NEVER BE THE SAME AGAIN

Words & Music by Melanie Chisholm, Rhett Lawrence, Paul F. Cruz, Lisa Lopes & Lorenzo Martin.

highways. See it'll never be the same, what I'm sayin' my mind frame never changed 'til you came and rearranged but

sometimes it seems completely forbidden to discover those feelings that we kept so well hidden where there's

no competition and you render my condition though improbable it's not impossible for a love that could be unstoppable but wait.

A fine line's between fate and destiny. Do you believe in the things that were just meant to be? When you

Verse 2:
Now I know that we were close before
I'm glad I realised I need you so much more
And I don't care what everyone will say
It's about you and me
And we'll never be the same again.

I thought that we would just be friends *etc.*

SUDDENLY MONDAY

Words & Music by Melanie Chisholm, Matt Rowe, Richard Stannard & Julian Gallagher.

1. Sud-den-ly Mon - day ap-pears— a - gain.___ Where was the week-
(Verse 2 see block lyric)

the things that you___ do.___ You make me

high,_____ I wish that you knew,___ I wish I could tell___

___ you. To - geth - er we'd fly,_____ op - en your eyes,___

start read - ing my___ mind.___ 2. Same con - ver - sa -

49

Na na na na na na————— na na na na.

Na na na na na na————— na na na na.

Repeat to fade

Verse 2:

Same conversation every day
So much to ask you but can't find a way
Wherever you're going can I come along?
Whatever your star sign, wherever you're from
The end of the day and you're still around
My head's in the clouds, feet on the ground
Maybe I should and maybe you would
Maybe tonight if only we could.

You make me high, I wish that you knew *etc.*

GA GA

Words & Music by Melanie Chisholm, Phil Thornalley & Dave Munday.

1. I don't want___ your a-do-ra-tion,
(Verses 2 & 3 see block lyrics)

don't want your train stop-pin' at my sta-tion. You hurt me___

Verse 2:
I don't want emotional hassle
I just want another bite of the apple
Dark thoughts need satisfaction
We're gonna crash
Let's make it happen.

Gaga *etc.*

Verse 3:
This will never be over
And you will always be mine
You've gotta feed my hunger baby
I am ready to dine.

Gaga *etc.*

BE THE ONE

Words & Music by Melanie Chisholm, Phil Thornalley & Dave Munday.

1. The si-tu-a-tion is get-ting bor - ing,_____ you're not___ gon-na spoil___ a-no-ther day._____
(Verse 2 see block lyric)

be the one, be the one who shares my hung-er and thirst. You see the

oth-er ones are hang-ing me, ooh they've got no-thing on you. You wan-na

be the one, be the one, the on-ly one.

I've got no time for bit-ter-ness, I wan-na move a-way from this.

59

Verse 2:

You say you're hooked on me
But where were you last night?
Because when you looked at me, yeah
You couldn't hold my eye
Saying things you never mean
It's no big surprise
Telling me that you're the one
I'm tired of the lies.

Be the one
Be the one who moves my heaven and earth *etc.*

CLOSER

Words & Music by Melanie Chisholm, Rick Nowels & Billy Steinberg.

1. Lov-ing you mad-ly will be for-ev-er. I see the o-cean in your eyes
(Verse 2 see block lyric)

How much love can— we make?

Flute

D.%. al Coda

⊕ Coda

(Clos - er._____)

- er._____   to_____

Verse 2:
Time passes by seconds into minutes
Every field and flower fades but love is infinite
There are no boundaries
There are no limits
My heart's a bigger place now that you're in it.

Hold me closer to your dreams *etc.*

FEEL THE SUN

Words & Music by Melanie Chisholm & Rick Nowels.

1. These thoughts can be ev - il and they of - ten de - ceive, got - ta be - lieve that I can ov - er - come. My fears are the worst and they al - ways re - turn, I nev - er learn. Feel like I don't be - long.

(Verse 2 see block lyrics)

2.

There's so much en - er - gy,___ at last I can be free.___

I am the per - son I___ was look - ing for.___

D.%. al Coda

⊕ *Coda*

I'm feel - ing strong,___ I'll___ nev - er fall. You are there when I

Verse 2:

Guilt is no use it will tarnish your soul
Just let it go
The battle will soon be won
Cold in the shadow of who I should be
There's a fire burning deep inside me
Helping me see, only I hold the key
And now I stand here unafraid
Proud of everything I've made
That's why I had to run away.

Feel the sun *etc.*

Exclusive distributors:
Music Sales Limited
8/9 Frith Street, London W1V 5TZ, England.
Music Sales Pty Limited
120 Rothschild Avenue, Rosebery, NSW 2018, Australia.

Order No. AM962126
ISBN 0-7119-7982-0
This book © Copyright 1999 by Wise Publications.

Music arranged by Derek Jones.
Music engraved by Paul Ewers.
Photographs courtesy of Virgin Records.

Printed in the United Kingdom.